My Broth... the Bridesmaid

Written by Jane Langford

Illustrated by Nick Schon

Chapter 1

Hi! My name is Daisy. You've never met me. You've never met my brother, Jo, either. Lucky you! You'd think I'd be used to him now, what with us being twins, but somehow he always ends up surprising me. Like the time he was a bridesmaid. That's right – a bridesmaid! I bet you'd like to know how *that* happened. Well ...

My Auntie Celia lives in Australia. She owns a posh restaurant by the sea. We've never seen her because she moved to Australia before Jo and I were born. Mum sent her a letter telling her all about us.

Hi Sis!
Here's a photo of my two
little bundles of joy: Daisy,
born 11th April at 2.10 am, quickly followed
by Jo at 2.24 am. They both weighed in
at 2.4 kg and look almost identical!
I can't wait for you to see them. Come
and visit us soon!
Love
Jasmine xx

Well, Auntie Celia never did come to visit, as she was always so busy with the restaurant. Mum said Auntie Celia hadn't had a holiday for at least ten years – imagine that! No wonder we didn't hear from her much.

Then one day, out of the blue, we got this letter:

Dear Jasmine,

I know it's been ages since I last wrote, but I have some exciting news. Geoffrey and I have decided to tie the knot! Isn't it fantastic? We've fixed the date for November 10th – I've always dreamed of a spring wedding – and of course you're all invited. In fact, it would mean the world to me if your girls would be my bridesmaids. What do you say? Let me know their sizes and I'll get the dresses made. They'll look divine!

I can't wait to see you and the children – it's been too long!

Lots of love

Celia

xx

Wow! A bridesmaid. I was so excited. Mum squeezed me
proudly.

"So, what do you think, kids?" she grinned. "Shall we go to
Australia?"

Amy chuckled and I nodded eagerly, but Jo was too busy
rolling around on the floor.

"A bridesmaid!" he choked, pointing at me. "How can she
be a bridesmaid? She's never put a dress on in her life!"

Chapter 2

On the day of the flight there was heavy fog at the airport. It might have been spring in Australia, but it was almost winter in England. Our plane was grounded until the fog cleared.

Luckily there was tons to do at the airport. We read comics, cruised round the shops and went to the café for a hot chocolate. Jo spent ages trying on sunglasses – he thought he looked so cool, too!

After a while though, Amy got fidgety and me and Jo
were just plain bored!

"I hope we're not delayed much longer!" grumbled Mum.

Finally we were allowed to board the plane, but things didn't get any better. Do you know how long it takes to fly to Australia? Well, I can tell you – it takes AGES!

Mum and Amy slept most of the way – lucky them! I don't know how they did it, it was so hot and uncomfortable. Jo and I watched three films, then we watched the first film again.

When our plane finally touched down in Sydney we were exhausted. It was nearly midnight on the day before the wedding.

Auntie Celia was there to meet us and she was in a terrible flap. "I thought you were never going to get here!" she squealed.

She hugged Jo and me so tightly we nearly burst.

Auntie Celia started talking about how she'd had the dresses made, and how lovely they were...

"You only sent me one set of measurements for the twins," she said. "So I guess they must be the same size. They're just like two peas in a pod. The dresses will be perfect!"

Jo's face turned as red as a raspberry. He looked desperately at Mum.

"What?" he muttered. "Does she think I'm a girl?"

"Um, er," Mum stuttered. "Let me introduce the twins. This is Daisy and..."

"This must be Joanna!" gushed Auntie Celia.

Mum gulped like a fish out of water. The words, "No, Joseph..." froze in her throat.

Suddenly a taxi pulled up beside us. There was no time for Mum's throat to melt.

"There's your car!" cried Auntie Celia. "It'll take you straight over to the hotel. Go and get yourselves a good night's sleep and I'll see you in the morning!"

When we got to our hotel room, we found the three dresses hanging in the wardrobe. They were exquisite.

"They must have cost a fortune!" gasped Mum.

"But they're PINK!" exploded Jo. "I am not going to wear a soppy pink dress for anyone's wedding."

"Pink's a lovely colour, Jo," I teased.

"I'm sorry, Jo," giggled Mum. "We can't spoil Auntie Celia's big day."

"What about it spoiling MY day!" Jo protested. "Everyone in Australia will think I'm a girl."

"Not everyone, silly," I said. "Just all the wedding guests!"

Chapter 3

Next morning, Mum got us all up early. She brushed our hair till it hurt, then helped us girls into our dresses. I'm not a big fan of frills, but I have to admit, we didn't look bad!

Jo sat on the bed and sulked.

"I don't want to go to the stupid wedding," he grumbled. "You could say I was sick."

Before Mum could react, there was a knock at the door.

Auntie Celia twirled into the room in her wedding gown.

"You look stunning, sis!" Mum gasped.

Even Jo looked impressed.

"I've just come to see my charming bridesmaids," sang Auntie Celia. "Oh, don't they look gorgeous?"

Then, she caught sight of Jo. "Hey, Joanna, you're not ready! Come on, I'll give you a hand."

Jo leapt off the bed like a lizard. "No!" he shouted. "Leave me alone!"

"What's wrong?" asked Auntie Celia. "Don't you like the dress? It's been made especially for you!"

"Um, well…" Jo stammered awkwardly. "I suppose it is quite nice… for a dress. It's just a bit… girly!"

Auntie Celia smiled sympathetically. "Oh! You're a bit of a tomboy, are you?"

"Sort of," said Jo.

"Never mind. I know you girls like to wear jeans these days, but this is my special day."

Jo shook his head stubbornly.

Tears sprang into Auntie Celia's eyes.

"But it's my wedding day," she wailed. "Please, just for me...?"

"No!" said Jo.

"Come on..." whined Auntie Celia. She puckered up her glossy pink lips and advanced on Jo with her arms outstretched. "Oh, alright!" he yelled. "If I HAVE to!"

And do you know, he did. My brother Jo put on that pink, frilly dress and walked down the aisle behind the bride with the rest of us. Honestly! What a sight! No one noticed that he wore clumping great trainers instead of pink ballet shoes, or if they did, they were too polite to say so.

The wedding was perfect and everyone said that the
bridesmaids looked enchanting.

Back at the hotel, Jo squirmed out of his dress and flung it on the bed.

"No one is to tell anyone about this, EVER!" he ordered.

A few weeks later, Mum got a letter from Auntie Celia.

Dear Jasmine,

Thanks so much for coming to the wedding. Geoffrey and I had a wonderful day! Thought you and the girls might like to see this — cut it out of the local paper.

Lots of love

Celia

xx

The Sydney Herald

Marriages

Geoffrey Arkwright and his bride, Celia, were married at the Seagrove Hotel on Saturday. The couple are shown here with their beautiful bridesmaids — English roses, all three!

"You see!" wailed Jo. "I told you everyone in Australia would think I was girl!"